# World Geography

## The world's
# Resources
## & their exploitation

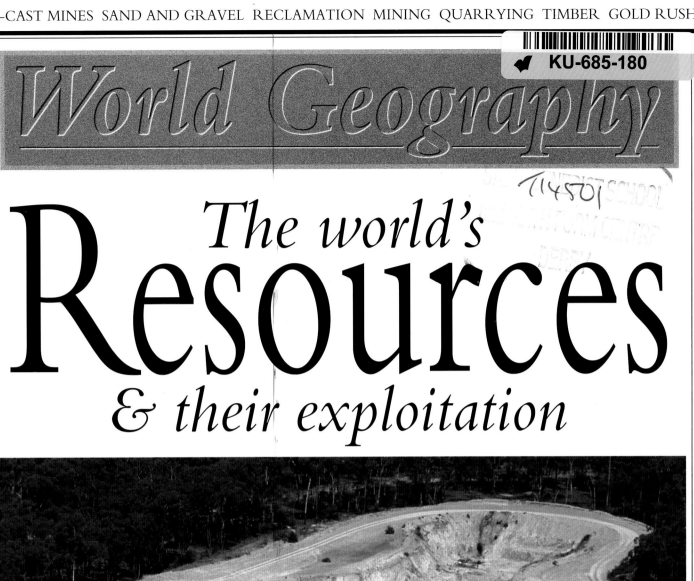

Atlantic Europe
Publishing

# How to use this book

There are many ways of using this book. Below you will see how each page is arranged to help you to find information quickly, revise main ideas or look for material in detail. The choice is yours!

On some pages you will find words that have been shown in CAPITALS. There is a full explanation of each of these words in the glossary on page 63.

This heading in the running text tells you about the section that follows.

This is the main column of running text that forms the chapter. Read this for a good understanding of the subject as a whole.

Scan these boxes for key ideas.

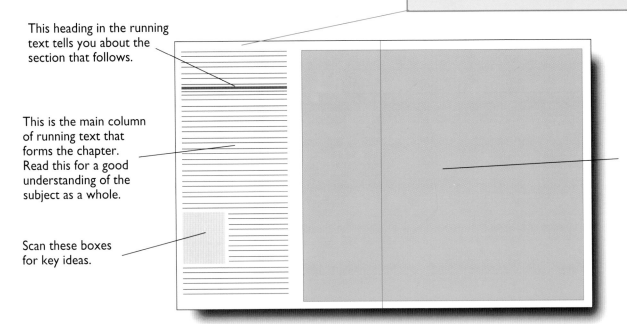

The information in the box describes an important subject in detail and gives additional facts.

**Author**
*Brian Knapp, BSc, PhD*
**Educational Consultant**
*Stephen Codrington, BA, DipEd, PhD*
**Art Director**
*Duncan McCrae, BSc*
**Editor**
*Elizabeth Walker, BA*
**Illustrators**
*Simon Tegg & David Woodroffe*
**Designed and produced by**
*EARTHSCAPE EDITIONS*
**Print consultants**
*Landmark Production Consultants Ltd*
**Printed and bound by**
*Paramount Printing Company Ltd*

First published in the United Kingdom in 1995 by Atlantic Europe Publishing Company Limited, 86 Peppard Road, Sonning Common, Reading, Berkshire, RG4 9RP, UK

The Atlantic Europe Publishing logo is a registered trademark of Atlantic Europe Publishing Company Limited.

**Suggested cataloguing location**

Knapp, Brian
    The world's resources and their exploitation
    – (World Geography; 8)
333.7

ISBN 1-869860-68-3

Acknowledgements
The publishers would like to thank the following for their help and advice: *Aspen Flying Club, Englewood, Colorado; Auburn Flight Service, Auburn, Washington; Bendigo Aviation Services, Victoria, Australia; Bridgeford Flying Service, Napa, California; Eveland Aero, Honolulu, Hawaii; David Newell, Oxfam-Bridge, Thailand; Lake County Airport, Leadville, Colorado; Oxfam, India; Oxfam, Kenya; The Pacific Lumber Company, Scotia, California; The Royal Commonwealth Society Collection, the Syndics of the Cambridge University Library, Cambridge, UK; Frank Sperling and Wycombe Aviation, UK.*

Picture credits
(c=centre t=top b=bottom l=left r=right)
All photographs are from the **Earthscape Editions** library except the following: **The Hutchison Library** 21 (*Michael Macintyre*); **British Petroleum International** 19tl; **The Pacific Lumber Company** 48cl, 49br, 50/51; **British Coal Corporation** 27br; by permission of **the Syndics of the Cambridge University Library** 2cr, 20br & 22tl (*Ernest Brown*); 10cr, 10br & 11tl (*A. Gill, 87 Victoria gold diggings and gold diggers*); 10/11 (*J. N. Macartney, The Bendigo Goldfield Registry*); 10bl, 11br, 22bl, 23tr, 46cl; **USGS** 23br; **Tony Waltham** 14, 20cr, 26b, 27t; **ZEFA** 16/17.

*This product is manufactured from sustainable managed forests. For every tree cut down at least one more is planted.*

# Contents

# Chapter 1

# Facts about resources

Everything we need – our resources – has to come from our planet, whether it is food, water, stone, metals, timber or fuels.

Sometimes people describe our planet as Spaceship Earth, because if we use up any one of Earth's resources then we will be without it forever.

In this chapter we look at some general principles of how resources are used and the effect this can have on our environment.

*(Note: some of Earth's resources, such as food and fuels, need special explanations and they are described in more detail in the books Farms and Energy in the World Geography series.)*

If we could drill a hole from the surface to the centre of the Earth, we would have drilled the gigantic distance of 6700 km. If we could use all the material that the Earth contains we would be able to call on 1.2 million million cubic kilometres of materials weighing 6600 million million million tonnes! This would be an almost limitless source of the things we need. Looked at on this scale, it would seem that the things that we have done in our entire history have not even scratched the surface.

❏ (left) Many resources can be gained from the environment in basically simple ways. Many techniques have been used since ancient times and are still appropriate today. Here, artificial lakes called salt pans are fed with sea water and the water allowed to evaporate away before more water is added. Eventually this natural process yields beds of salt that can be scraped away with a bulldozer.

But it is not quite that simple. Despite all of our modern science and technology, people cannot drill to great depths. Even drills to 20 or 30 kilometres take the most advanced machines. And besides, so far we have only learned how to make use of a small amount of the material the Earth has to offer.

## Pressure on resources

Partly because it is so hard to obtain materials from the Earth, people have concentrated on making the most of the materials that exist on the surface, using clay for bricks, gravel and limestone for concrete, forests for timber and plants for food. The result is that we have often put an intolerable burden on these resources, causing great harm to the natural environment.

> The world contains a wide variety of materials – minerals, timber and water, for example – that can be made useful. These are called resources.

You can get a feel for the amount of various materials that we use by looking at the resources needed for homes, shown in the panel on page 9.

In fact, most of the materials we use in our homes are used quite efficiently. We use nearly all of the material taken from the trees or from the ground. Other processes are by no means as efficient, such as removing minerals from ores; and many of our habits are even more wasteful, such as not helping to recycle resources after we have used them.

## Resources that boom and bust

There is one very basic point to note about many of the world's reserves of resources. It is a harsh fact that causes great hardship to many people, but it is inescapable: the amount of a material at any one place is not everlasting.

## What are the Earth's resources?

The Earth's resources – raw materials that we can use to make other things – consist of rock, soil, water, air, plants and animals.

Most of the Earth's materials are so mixed up that we do not have the techniques to sort them out and make them useful. We just call them 'rock'. Much of the material we do know how to use is buried deep within the Earth and completely out of our reach. So our practical choices are not that great after all. In effect, we can use just a small number of substances on or near the Earth's surface. And the less there is of these substances, and the harder they are to find, the more they are worth. The most precious of all are the rarities of the world: gemstones, oil, fresh water and gold. People have even started wars to gain these resources.

❒ (above) There is much argument about whether old forests should be cut down and used for timber. But it doesn't have to be a choice between timber and jobs or conservation and wildlife. Timber can be harvested so that some trees are always left to grow old and provide a home for wildlife. If we think far enough ahead, we can avoid passing on mistakes, and eventually please everyone.

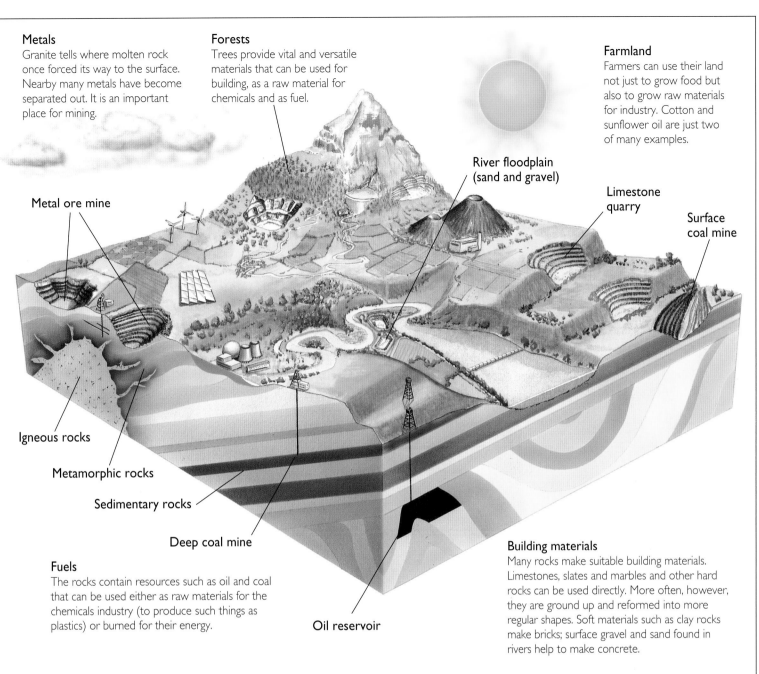

**Metals**
Granite tells where molten rock once forced its way to the surface. Nearby many metals have become separated out. It is an important place for mining.

**Forests**
Trees provide vital and versatile materials that can be used for building, as a raw material for chemicals and as fuel.

**Farmland**
Farmers can use their land not just to grow food but also to grow raw materials for industry. Cotton and sunflower oil are just two of many examples.

Metal ore mine

River floodplain (sand and gravel)

Limestone quarry

Surface coal mine

Igneous rocks

Metamorphic rocks

Sedimentary rocks

Deep coal mine

**Fuels**
The rocks contain resources such as oil and coal that can be used either as raw materials for the chemicals industry (to produce such things as plastics) or burned for their energy.

Oil reservoir

**Building materials**
Many rocks make suitable building materials. Limestones, slates and marbles and other hard rocks can be used directly. More often, however, they are ground up and reformed into more regular shapes. Soft materials such as clay rocks make bricks; surface gravel and sand found in rivers help to make concrete.

❒ (left) In the past, it was thought that only poor people needed to recycle goods. However, more and more people are coming to understand that, rich or poor, we all need to recycle materials for the good of the planet. The Earth's resources are not limitless.

It will run out. When it does there is no longer any need for the people who extracted it, for example miners or lumberjacks. There is also far less income for the towns they live in.

> We take our resources too much for granted, using them too quickly with little thought of tomorrow. This has created towns which grow rapidly (boom towns) but which decay in a short time (ghost towns).

This process can best be described as 'boom and bust'. People discover a material they want and they extract it as fast as they can (boom times). Then the resource runs out (bust times). In the famous gold rushes of the 19th century, bust followed boom in a matter of a few years in countries as widely scattered as the United States, South Africa and Australia, leaving behind ghost towns. In the coal fields of Europe, the boom and bust cycle has taken two centuries and has gradually left hundreds of thousands of people unemployed.

# Never rely on a resource

Boom and bust explain why it is important not to rely on a resource. Many countries depend on mining some kind of resource. For example, two thirds of Jamaica's export earnings come from mining and processing bauxite, the ore that gives aluminium. Copper makes up over 90 per cent of Zambia's exports, and minerals account for 70 per cent of all exports by value in Indonesia, 99 per cent in Libya and 90 per cent in Nigeria.

These countries know the peril this brings. Bolivia, for example, where four-tenths of overseas earnings come from the sale of tin, fell into serious debt when the world price of tin fell sharply in 1986. Nigeria, too, is in debt because the price it can get for oil is now far lower than it was just a few years ago.

## Resources just to build homes

Everyone needs resources. For example, have you ever thought where your home comes from, what it is made of and its impact on the world around you?

The example that follows gives you a feel for the resources needed to build a house. But remember, houses can be very different from place to place, so these figures are just a guide.

In a city of 1 million people there may be a quarter of a million homes. That means a quarter of a million piles of building materials.

The base for each home uses up 22.5 million cubic metres of material from the ground. The concrete is a mixture of about 1 part cement, 8 parts stones and sand, and 1 part water. The material taken from the ground to make a pit the same height as a house (8 m) would have an area of 2.8 million sq. m or 2.8 sq. km. That is, the hole would be just under 3 km by 1 km.

To make walls measuring 8 m x 10 m x 8 m each, and 60 cm thick (and including internal walls), requires about 400 cubic metres of material. If the house is mostly built of bricks then the material needed would create a hole 4.5 times the size of the foundation.

Overall, the city would need to use materials from a hole 5.5 km x 3 km x 8 m deep.

For wooden frames and rafters, perhaps 4 medium-sized softwood trees would be needed per house; that's 1 million trees for the whole city. If the whole house were wood, the amount would be far greater. Trees are spaced about 4 m apart, so the area of forest needed to provide wood for brick-built homes would be 4 million sq. m, 4 sq. km.

You can see how much of the Earth's resources are needed for modern living. Using this as a guide, you can find out how many resources your own home area uses.

❐ (below) Concrete is made with limestone, which has to be quarried from the ground. Sand and gravel are also needed, perhaps a pit 8 m deep, 3 km x 1 km, for the concrete.

*Chapter 3: Quarries*

❐ (left) Chicago is a city of 8 million people, so its building materials requirements might be 8 times the figures suggested here.

❐ (below) Trees used for rafters and floorboards, might require about 4 sq. km of forest to be felled.

# Chapter 5: Forests

❐ (left) A city of 1 million people might spread across an area 30 km x 30 km, 900 sq. km. The land for roads, houses and other urban uses was once the resource called farmland.

# Chapter 2: Minerals

# Chapter 6: Water

❐ (above) Homes also need water. To provide a clean, reliable supply of water, large areas of land have to be set aside for reservoirs.

❐ (above) Homes contain a wide range of materials, for example plastic and steel. To manufacture these resources, raw materials have to be won from the ground and then processed.

# Vital today, worthless tomorrow?

You might think that we already know how to use the world's resources, but this is not so. This is because needs and values change. A good example of this is the metal uranium. Until the nuclear industry was developed it was just a useless element; now it is a prized source of energy and natural resource.

> We must now take a longer term view of resources and begin to conserve and recycle. But this approach can lead to a low demand and, thus, loss of jobs.

The reverse is also true. People may ignore a valuable resource once a better substitute is found. For example in the STONE AGE, flints were used as axes, and the rock which contained it was highly valued. But later, iron blades could be made, and flint was no longer wanted; today flints are just worthless rocks.

Resources have different values to different peoples. In Britain water is plentiful and thus is less prized as a resource than it is in countries near the Sahara Desert, in central Australia or in the southwest United States.

◻ (above) A prospector's dream! The gold nugget 'Perseverance' was found in the South African province of Natal on 16 December 1874. It weighed 3.3 kg and was just over 12 cm long. News of discoveries such as this spread fast and attracted people from around the world who risked everything for the chance to strike it rich.

# An example of boom and bust: the growth of a goldrush town

Through the ages gold has held such a powerful attraction for people that, even in an age when communications were poor, news of a gold strike would travel like wildfire.

Thousands of ordinary people packed up their belongings to try to strike it rich. Some would even walk hundreds or thousands of kilometres for a chance to stake a claim.

These pictures show the growth of a goldrush town in Bendigo, Australia. Similar scenes could be found in the United States, Canada, and South Africa, all of which had gold strikes in the 19th century.

1 Before the miners arrived the land was countryside. But soon small towns sprung up. Most miners were men. In a few cases they brought their entire family, and the women helped with the panning.

The basic gear of a miner was the gold pan and pick. Tents and bedding were luxuries. Some miners travelled by cart, most walked.

2 As stakes were made and gold found, there was money to be made by those offering basic services such as selling groceries or renting out spaces in tent cities. Many of the shopkeepers grew wealthier than the miners.

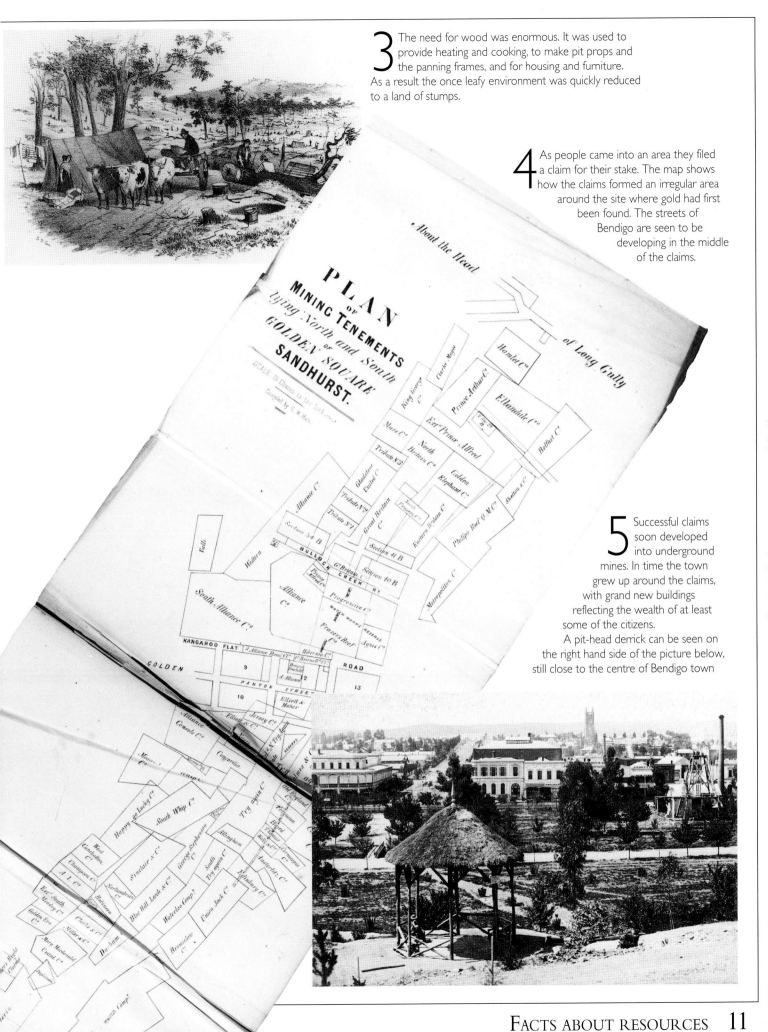

**3** The need for wood was enormous. It was used to provide heating and cooking, to make pit props and the panning frames, and for housing and furniture. As a result the once leafy environment was quickly reduced to a land of stumps.

**4** As people came into an area they filed a claim for their stake. The map shows how the claims formed an irregular area around the site where gold had first been found. The streets of Bendigo are seen to be developing in the middle of the claims.

**5** Successful claims soon developed into underground mines. In time the town grew up around the claims, with grand new buildings reflecting the wealth of at least some of the citizens.
A pit-head derrick can be seen on the right hand side of the picture below, still close to the centre of Bendigo town

PLAN
OF
MINING TENEMENTS
lying North and South
OF
GOLDEN SQUARE
SANDHURST.

SCALE 10 Chains to the Inch

Compiled by C. W. Hart

Industrial world countries think of mud as a nuisance, not a resource. Yet throughout much of the developing world it is a valuable building material known as adobe.

Almost anything can be considered a resource – land, water, minerals, even people. Yet it is nothing until a demand is created, and that demand can fall just as easily as it arises.

# The many faces of a resource

The rainforests of the tropics show how different people can see the same resource in different ways:

☛ The native peoples of rainforests see trees as a source of food, fuel, building materials, clothing and medicines.

> Resources are attractive to people for many reasons. Some see them as a way to make money, others as a way to help people improve their lives. Many people worry that using the land at all spoils the environment.

☛ Settlers wishing to cut down the trees think the rainforest is useless. Instead they (mistakenly) believe that soil is the most important resource, because they desperately need to grow crops to feed themselves.

☛ Miners think both the trees and the soil are useless because they seek riches from the rocks below.

☛ Logging companies see the trees as a source of the timber which can be sold for profits.

☛ Scientists see the forest as a valuable store of natural variety to be preserved and studied.

☛ And environmentalists see the rainforest as a natural environment to be preserved simply for itself, as a resource called 'wilderness'.

It is no wonder, when people see the same thing in so many ways, that arguments may arise.

# Ghost towns of a goldrush age

Resources do not last forever. If a community's survival depends on a resource, that community will decay as the resource goes bust. The gold and silver rushes of 19th-century America, for example, caused the population of remote areas of Nevada, California, Arizona and Alaska to boom. However, as soon as the resource had been worked out, the people moved away, leaving only ghost towns in their wake. Modern towns have not suffered such a dramatic decline, but they have seen their fortunes subside, leaving a sense of sadness around the community.

❐ Goldfield, Nevada, is a small city in the United States. At one time it boasted a fine town hall (shown above), grand shops and a thriving, if somewhat rowdy, frontier community. Now the gold mines have been worked out and just a few people cling to the remnants of the town. The small saloon (shown below) is one of the remaining buildings open for business.

□ (left) When people finally abandon the mineral workings there is usually no money for cleaning up the mess. This gold dredger has been abandoned in the pit it once worked near Bendigo, Australia.

□ (below) The pit head winding frame where people once went to work in search of gold in Goldfield.

# Can resources last forever?

This century has seen a dramatic growth in the population and with it a larger demand for resources. It is easy to understand why so many people are worried about which resources will be left in the future. Developing countries still have lower demands than industrial countries, but they are certain to use more resources as they grow.

The resources that are most important to us today (petroleum, coal, metals, etc.) can only be replaced by Nature after many millions of years. We call these resources non-renewable.

On the other hand, some resources renew themselves more quickly, such as plants grown for food, building materials and fuel. We call these renewable resources. But they too can be used up too fast if we do not use them carefully.

There are two ways the future might develop:

☛ The population could continue to grow fast, using up minerals and forests, and polluting the Earth.

☛ The population could eventually level off. New resources might be discovered and substances that were once thought of as unusable could become important new products.

Either way, it is up to us to use resources carefully.

> The use of resources causes more conflict than almost anything on Earth: wars are fought over them and they can make a country rich or poor. But their exploitation also causes concern about pollution and other kinds of environmental damage.

# Boom or bust for the developing world?

Many countries in the DEVELOPING WORLD have large resources of minerals and timber. However, they do not have the need, or perhaps the means, to use all the resources in their own country. It then becomes very tempting to sell the resources overseas and buy oil, food or other goods in exchange. Some developing world countries, such as the oil-rich states of North Africa and the Middle East, have been able to provide their people with great wealth this way.

However, people who sell minerals or timber depend on the price they can get from industrial countries. This can change quickly and cause many problems. For example, the oil-rich countries did well when the oil price was high. However, in recent years the price of oil has fallen and this has left oil countries far less wealthy.

As you look around the world you can find many more examples. Bolivia, for example, depends heavily on exporting tin ores mined from the Andes mountains. When the world tin price crashed suddenly some years ago, the whole country was nearly ruined.

The lesson is this: a country cannot depend on getting wealthier by selling its resources. It must try to use the resources, to develop a variety of industries so that the boom will never suddenly change to bust.

## Bauxite and Jamaica

Bauxite is aluminium ore. For many uses it competes with steel and copper. The main Bauxite mining areas are found in the tropics. It is especially important to small countries like Jamaica.

aluminium ore

Bauxite is mined in open-cast pits in much the same way as coal is sometimes mined. After it has been mined it still has to be refined, an expensive process that uses a lot of electricity.

Jamaica produces about an eighth of the world's bauxite. Its export has helped to employ many people and bring revenue into the country. But since the late 1970s Jamaica has faced serious problems. It relies on imported oil to provide the energy necessary to process the bauxite and this has become more expensive. World demand for aluminium has also dropped as more aluminium is recycled. This leaves the future prosperity from bauxite very uncertain.

❐ (above and right) This is the town of Taxco in Mexico where the first silver mine in the western hemisphere was opened. The wealth of the town reflects how the silver was exploited, first by the Spanish colonial government and then by the Mexican people. There is still a silver mine in the town, but it employs just a small part of the population. For all the others, the boom is over and they have to find work elsewhere.

The building in the centre of the picture is simply a church (although it may look as grand as a cathedral), but it was built by a miner to whom money was no object.

❐ (left) When your livelihood depends on mining a resource, it is unlikely you will think too far into the future. This pyrite mine in Sichuan, China, will be worked as hard as possible because the local people depend on it. After that? . . . It's a case of letting the future take care of itself.

# Chapter 2

# Mining

Most of the wide range of minerals and building materials used by people have to be dug from the ground.

Although nature has concentrated minerals in many ways, most useful materials are still often found among large amounts of useless waste. To get the materials as efficiently as possible, miners have adopted many techniques, but miners are most successful when they understand how the materials were formed.

Many of the world's resources are taken from the Earth. Mining is the term used to describe the working of useful minerals, such as coal, oil, metals and salt, from open pits or from underground.

Usually the minerals have to be extracted from beds of rock known as ore or mineral deposits. In the past these deposits had to contain very high concentrations of useful materials for mining to be worthwhile; today, modern processes can extract even tiny amounts of useful material from rock, but the effect on the environment is far greater.

The word quarrying is used only to describe the removal of stone, sand, gravel or other building materials from an open site. Sites for stone are often deep and are called quarries; those for clay, sand and gravel are usually shallow and are known as pits.

❏ (left) Copper mining at Mt Isa, Queensland. The mine is deep underground, although large amounts of land are needed at the surface for the processing plant, railways, and for storage of the waste rock. Very often huge amounts of ore are mined for only tiny quantities of metal.

# The earliest mines

The history of mining goes back at least 40,000 years, when ancient peoples used hard rocks called flints to make hand axes and arrow heads, and coloured (ironstone) rock for decoration and for their cave paintings. This was the Stone Age.

Metal ores are most easily recovered from the beds of rivers or from concentrated deposits called veins.

The first metals to be used were those that had been loosened from the rocks in which they were formed. Most of these were found in small pieces among the sand and gravel of river beds. They are known as PLACER DEPOSITS.

Many pure metals are heavier than stone, and they can be separated from the river bed by panning. Panning is the oldest form of mining in history.

# Easily used metals

Gold, still thought of as the world's most precious metal, was used by the ancient Egyptians to make, among other things, a likeness of the boy king Tutankhamen, still one of the world's artistic masterpieces. Gold was useful because it does not tarnish and because of its beauty. It is also soft, melts at low temperatures and so it is very easy to work.

However, gold is rare, and for many more everyday things, ancient civilisations also used more common metals such as copper.

Copper occurs as thin irregularly shaped bands, or veins, of metal which can sometimes be found among beds of rock at the surface. They may have first been spotted in a stream bank or a sea cliff.

Copper is harder than gold and it could be used to make weapons as well as bowls and other cooking utensils.

# Where ores are found

An ore is a rock that contains enough metal or mineral to make mining it profitable.

The richest ores contain veins of pure material and are found in mountains. Most ores, however, contain quite small amounts of pure minerals or metals mixed up in SEDIMENTARY rocks. Iron, for example, is often found mixed in with limestone and sandstone, where it gives these rocks a yellow, red or brown colour.

Modern society depends heavily upon raw materials produced from various types of ore deposits. Machines are made from metals, and even our food depends on using chemical fertilizers made from minerals.

Nature concentrates minerals in few places, which tells us that unusual geological conditions must have occurred. For example, ores are common near where molten rock (magma) pushed towards the Earth's surface. It is thought that some of the world's richest ore deposits lie on the sea bed near undersea volcanoes.

Ores on land can be even more concentrated if the ore-rich rocks are later eroded by rivers. The heavier metals will settle out on the river bed or along a nearby seashore.

❒ (below) Natural erosion of the land breaks up the ore and carries it to the sea in small pieces, along with other river sediment. Metals are heavier than rock, so they settle in the river beds as placer deposits.

❒ (above) Many very pure ores form near masses of molten rock. As fingers of molten rock force their way through cracks, they heat up water in the surrounding rocks, making it very acidic. Most metals dissolve in extremely hot acidic water, so as the water filters through the rock and cools, the minerals come out of solution one at a time, forming veins. This is the reason gold, silver, copper, tin and lead can often be found at various levels in a single mine. This is a gold-bearing vein in an Australian gold mine. A large piece of gold found in an ore is called a nugget.

❒ (right) This copper ore has been formed under great heat and pressure during the formation of a mountain. The metal content may be two-thirds or more of the vein in which it occurs. It is worth following this vein underground and extracting the ore by deep mining.

copper ore

❒ (below and left) This is iron ore in a sedimentary rock. It has been laid down under the sea and now occurs in thick beds. The iron content of this kind of ore is low, perhaps less than a third of the ore. It has be processed in a blast furnace (left) until all of the waste rock is removed.

❒ (left) This is a molybdenum mine. The mineral is found in tiny quantities that can only be extracted with the most modern equipment. To get just small quantities of the mineral whole mountain-sides have to be mined away, causing changes in the landscape and possible pollution in nearby rivers and lakes.

iron ore

# Bronze and Iron

Bronze, a mixture, called an alloy, of copper and tin, began to be used about 5000 years ago (The BRONZE AGE). Tin, like copper, is found in veins of nearly pure metal and will melt at a relatively low temperature. Bronze is harder than copper and it was favoured for over a thousand years.

Iron is more difficult to melt than copper or tin and it could not be used until people learned to make hotter fires. But by about 4000 years ago small pieces of pure iron were being collected from stream beds and heated until it was soft enough to be beaten into crude shapes. Thus began the IRON AGE.

> Mining by hand has made some poor people very rich. In countries like Brazil, many will still try their luck in the rainforests.

Only a small amount of iron can be gained from streams, so it was not long before iron mining began. Underground mining probably began in the European Alps about 3500 years ago, and in the Nubian desert of Africa 3000-year-old iron-mine shafts have been found that appear to have descended to depths of nearly 100 m.

## Mining by hand

The mining industry is unusual. It does not contain an even spread of mines of all different sizes. Instead, most mining is done by large corporate mining companies. But curiously enough, mining also happens on a very small scale, because people have often tried their luck at mining in the hope that they would 'strike it rich'.

To mine successfully by hand, prospectors have to find a rich ore. This may be a vein in a rock, or it may be placer deposits where nature has deposited heavy metals like gold in easily reached river beds.

The tools needed for basic mining are few: a pick and shovel and a sack to carry the ore away. People trying their luck in a placer deposit would also need a shallow metal dish called a pan.

Ore was still transported through the mines by human (and sometimes animal) power during the mid-19th century, and women often carried the broken ore in baskets and up ladders in the shafts, or pushed wagons along rail tracks.

All mine tasks are difficult and dangerous, although improvements – including underground coal-cart tracks, steam hoists, and the power drill – made working conditions somewhat better. Nevertheless, it remains back-breaking work.

❐ (above) Mining a thin seam of pyrite in China. The conditions in this mine are terrible and the single pit prop is far too weak to make the roof safe. These irregular seams are often dug by hand because there is not enough money to buy machinery.

❐ (left) Washing river gravels in the search for gold. Canada, 1890s.

❐ (left) Modern-day goldrush fever in Brazil. This is the Sierra Pelada mine. Its owner sells rock from the mine to each peasant (galimpero) by the sack full. A few have become very rich, but most leave the area poorer than when they arrived.

As the centuries went past, more and more metal was needed. The Greeks and the Romans operated large mines. After the collapse of the Roman Empire, mining declined in the West, and China became one of the world's great centres of iron-making. By the 11th century the Chinese were making over 35,000 tonnes of iron a year. The Chinese used metals for such things as tools and bells, but they needed metal most of all for weapons.

> The need to mine deeper, and the cost of powered machinery changed mining from an industry of many small private mines into one dominated by large corporate mines.

## The mining industry

By the MIDDLE AGES, mining had become an industry; mine owners employed teams of workers. Some people became very skilled in

## Mining comes of age

Mining can be done by hand to recover ores near the surface. But many resources are not conveniently placed; they either need to be worked at great depth or occur in small deposits. Only well organised mines can work in these conditions, so inevitably mining has become purely a large-scale industry.

The pictures on this page illustrate the changes that occurred in many of the mining areas that were opened up by lucky strikes.

(below) Early mining was not a large-scale affair, but was run by many independent owners. As a result, the amount of money put into the mine was small. This picture shows a 19th-century mine in Edmonton, Canada.

2 (above) Mining depended on large amounts of labour to do everything from mine the resource to tow away the waste rock or fix pit props. When many people worked on neighbouring claims the result was near chaos.

3 (left) As the surface lodes were worked out, mining moved underground and the scene changed. Here you can still see the remains of abandoned surface workings, but there are very few people to be seen, because most of them are underground. Each pit shaft is marked by a derrick.

4 (right) By the 1920s mines had become much more mechanised. Trains could carry away ores and bring in supplies or fuels. Shafts, pumps, crushing plants and the like were run by machines, often driven by electricity, not steam. Mining had almost entered the modern age.

finding sites for mines, called prospecting, and could hire out their services, others became experts at mining, shoring up dangerous tunnels, and so on. But the average miner had to work in conditions that were dangerous for very little money.

As miners followed the pattern of natural deposits, they excavated complexes of deep vertical shafts and long tunnels (adits or galleries). This meant that a network of tunnels had to be made safe, and there had to be ways of getting the ore to the surface.

> Mines are complex industrial units employing large numbers of people above and below ground.

But mining was not just a matter of tunnelling away and shoring up the roof and walls. There were other problems, too. Even solid rocks are not watertight, and water seeps into almost all mines.

Draining the water is not a problem if the tunnels are horizontal, because the water flows naturally out of the tunnel. But deep mines with vertical shafts have no natural outlet for the water to drain away, and mines risked being flooded unless they were drained day and night.

This was a very urgent and difficult problem. All kinds of machines were used to try to get rid of the water. Eventually it was the invention of the steam engine that made deep mines possible. Produced by Thomas Savery in England in 1699, the world's first steam engine was called the Miner's Friend, and was later much improved by Thomas Newcomen and then James Watt.

Getting fresh air into a mine was another important problem. Air does not circulate well in mines, so some means of pumping fresh air had to be found. This was especially important in coal mines, because coal seams release poisonous and explosive gases.

## How early deep mines worked

A deep mine was a complex of many shafts and horizontal tunnels (adits) that were extended farther and farther in search of ore. Providing ventilation for the miners, transporting ore and waste rock out of the mine and keeping the mine dry were all problems encountered in deep mining.

Ventilation was achieved by sinking more than one shaft and by using pumps. Another system was to set a fire below ventilation shafts which sent up hot air and forced cool, fresh air down the main shaft. Drainage and transporting the ore to the surface were only successfully managed with machines.

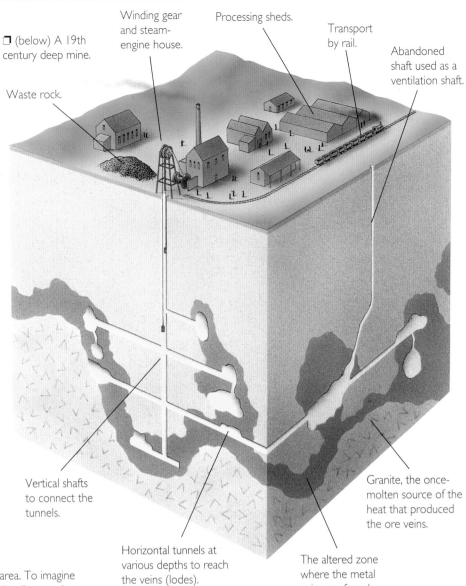

(below) A 19th century deep mine.

Winding gear and steam-engine house.

Processing sheds.

Transport by rail.

Abandoned shaft used as a ventilation shaft.

Waste rock.

□ (above) Traditional wooden supports for the tunnels of a small mine. The rail tracks were for hand-pushed trucks.

□ (left) The steam-engine house of a tin mine in Cornwall, England. The mine was abandoned after the tin veins were exhausted.

Vertical shafts to connect the tunnels.

Granite, the once-molten source of the heat that produced the ore veins.

□ (below) An abandoned mine area. To imagine how it worked, compare it with the diagram above.

Horizontal tunnels at various depths to reach the veins (lodes).

The altered zone where the metal veins are found.

Two solutions were used. In some mines, air was forced along pipes. In others, fires were burned at the bottom of special ventilation shafts. This made hot air rise through the ventilation shaft and caused cold, fresh air to be sucked in through the main shaft.

# The Industrial Revolution

The INDUSTRIAL REVOLUTION, which began in England in the 18th century, caused a great demand for all kinds of materials, especially iron, copper, lead, zinc, nickel and tin. The demand was so great that it could not be supplied by the traditional mining areas of Europe. Thus, the Industrial Revolution caused a worldwide search for new supplies of ores.

The Industrial Revolution created an immense demand for resources and sent people searching the globe for new deposits.

During the Industrial Revolution, another, much less publicised, revolution was under way. This was the chemical revolution. It had a very important effect on mining, because scientists were able to show that there were useful amounts of metals in many rocks, and that they could be extracted from their ores using chemical methods. As a result, people began to be able to use ores where they were less concentrated.

Within a short period of this revolution, the whole scale of mining changed. Less-rich ores had to be delivered in larger quantities, so, where before rocks had been broken up by burning fires against them until they cracked, by the 19th century whole rock faces were being blasted away, even deep underground, and the ore carried to works for processing using machines.

## Mining underground

There are many special problems to mining underground. One of the most important is to prevent the roof from caving in, called stoping.

When mining involves cutting into the ore, the area around the working face is supported with timber or steel props. As the ore is mined the supports are removed from areas that are no longer being worked, allowing the ground to subside naturally. In some mines a lot of waste rock has to be cut away to reach the ore. The waste is often fed back into the last area worked before its props are removed. This is called the *cut and fill* method.

In some cases thick blocks of unmined ground are left as natural supports for the mine workings. When the area around the block has been mined, the block is also mined out and the ground allowed to subside under its own weight. This is called *block caving*.

Many high-technology systems are used in underground mines. For example, to blast the ore clear, the working face is first drilled and then explosives pushed into the drill holes. The explosives are then fired and the broken rock is removed by excavators and conveyor belts.

In coal mines machines are brought up to a coal face and used to cut the coal and load it onto conveyors. New hydraulic props are then inserted behind the machine as it advances on the face.

□ (above) Mining equipment varies enormously. In the picture above the mine has tunnels large enough for dump-trucks to move through them. Where there is less space (below, right), or the mineral seam is very thin, the face is mined with special machines and the mineral is carried through the shaft on conveyor belts.

□ (above) The winding gear at the top of a deep mine.

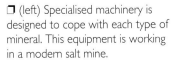

□ (left) Specialised machinery is designed to cope with each type of mineral. This equipment is working in a modern salt mine.

# Mining with machines

Machines allowed mining to change dramatically. Pit ponies were replaced by locomotives. Hand working at the active mine face was replaced by blasting equipment or by huge automated cutting machines. Small trucks that had been hauled away from the mine face by women and children, were replaced by conveyor belts.

> Wherever possible, mining is done from the surface. Not only is it safer, it is also cheaper, despite the amount of spoil that must be moved.

However, many old mines could not easily be adapted for use by machines. Miners working by hand had been able to work thin seams of ore or coal; modern machines are best suited to thick seams. The result has been that the mines with the thinner seams have not been able to reduce their costs and stay competitive, and many have had to close. This has affected both the miners and the other people in the mining towns, no matter whether it was coal, gold, iron or tin being mined.

But even the largest underground machines are no match for the giant machines that can be used to work on the surface. The trend to using bigger and bigger machines has therefore led to a search for ores that are close to the surface. The surface rock can be stripped away with giant diggers and the ore carried away directly by conveyor. In this way, many of the expensive techniques of deep mining can be done away with.

The change from deep mining to surface, or strip, mining has had the same effect as when machines replaced people at the mine face. It has meant that many of the traditional mining areas have lost jobs and some have closed completely.

## Surface mining

Surface mining costs much less than underground mining. There are two main ways that people mine on the surface. Huge dredgers can be used to excavate stream beds or estuaries for placer deposits. The excavated material is then washed to recover metals such as gold and tin and minerals such as diamonds. Thousands of tonnes a day may be washed by a single machine. However, dredging stirs up sediment and, in tropical waters especially, it can kill the animals on coastal reefs.

Another way of surface mining, called *strip mining*, excavates open pits. The overlying waste rock and soil – known as the overburden – is stripped away and piled nearby. Then a number of benches or terraces are dug, which slope and connect so that machines can carry the ore to the top of the pit. The same techniques are used when making roads or buildings. In fact, these mines are often worked by construction companies.

The ore is drilled and blasted so that excavators can carry it away. The working faces in this case are the walls of the terraces, so no expensive stoping is needed. The use of explosives on the surface requires far less skill than when they are used underground, and much larger amounts of ore can be blasted clear with each firing.

The scale of the machines that carry away the blasted ore is staggering. A single scoop can contain 50 cubic metres of material weighing more than 100 tonnes. The dump-trucks used to transport the ore can each be the size of a house, and each is capable of carrying more than 100 tonnes.

Strip mining opens up large areas of ground, and in the past caused widespread disfigurement of the landscape. Today, land is reclaimed after use. Pits are normally open for about 5 years before they are filled in and another site opened up.

❐ (below) Open-cast mining proceeds by blasting out layers and then carrying away the broken ore.

☐ (left) Large dump-trucks are used to carry the ore to the processing plants or to a railway for transport elsewhere.

☐ (below) This is a gold mine in Victoria, Australia, being worked by open-cast methods. The shape of the excavation is controlled by the location of the ore. Notice the trucks get in and out of the mine along ramps.

☐ (right) The most common way to excavate blasted rock is with a drag line on a mobile crane.

# Chapter 3

# Quarrying

Stone has been used for building since the earliest times. Some of the world's most famous structures, such as the pyramids, are made with a colossal amount of stone blocks.

There is still a need for some stone blocks as facings for buildings, but it is now used mainly for concrete or to make firm foundations beneath buildings and highways.

Meanwhile the need to quarry for brick-making clay is greater than ever.

Quarries provide building and pottery materials. The stone, clay, sand and gravel needed for construction are found widely, so traditionally quarries have supplied only their local areas. In addition, unlike mining for high-value minerals, quarries produce low-value, bulky and heavy material. Long journeys with this kind of material add greatly to their costs.

## Stone

Quarrying for stone is the most difficult and expensive way to gather building materials. In the past stone was used to make important buildings, and that is still its chief use today.

In buildings, only good-quality stone can be used, but because few quarries can produce suitable stone, it has a high value. This means

❐ (left) A slate quarry in England.

❐ (right) Stone, gravel, sand and clay are bulky materials for everyday uses. Traditionally, most resources were quarried and used locally to keep the expense of transport low. Pottery, for example is a major user of clay. Most potteries are near to good clay pits.

that it is worthwhile transporting stone considerable distances.

Decorative rocks, like marble, sandstone, granite and limestone, are quite rare. These materials are chosen for their fine grain or pattern and also the ease with which they can be cut away from the quarry. Decorative rock cannot be found near every settlement, so it is cut into sheets and used as facings for buildings. In this way the cost of transport is not as great as if the stone were moved in solid blocks.

Only decorative and special stones, such as limestone, marble and slate, are carried long distances.

Slate is a special rock that splits (cleaves) into sheets very easily and makes good natural roofing. Again, this is an uncommon rock, so slate often has to be transported long distances to meet demand.

# Aggregate

The vast majority of stone is not used whole but as rubble, known as aggregate. It is used, for example, to make the stone bulk of concrete or to make a base for buildings and roads.

Stone that is used for aggregate does not have to be of high quality and it does not have to be treated with the same care as in a quarry producing whole stone. This makes it very much cheaper.

Aggregate is made by blasting a quarry face using explosives. The broken rock is then carried to crushing plants where it is reduced to coarse, medium and fine sizes to meet different construction needs.

# Stone from rivers, ice and the sea

Blasting rock to make aggregate is expensive. But nature itself has many ways of breaking stone into small pieces. The main agents are

## Quarrying for stone

Quarries have to be located where there is suitable rock. In general, they are found in places where hard rocks occur at the surface. One of the most widely quarried rocks is limestone. Its main use, when crushed, is to make the base for roads. Harder rocks, such as volcanic rocks, are used to make chips used in road surfaces.

Crushed rock is also used as the coarse aggregate that forms the bulk of concrete for buildings.

❏ (above) Rock for road-making is blasted from the quarry face, rock for decorative purposes is prised away more carefully.

❏ (right) After many years of use, quarries and their waste piles can occupy large amounts of land. Decorative stone is unusual in being wasteful of materials, because only perfect stone is worth sending out for sale. Slate, for example, has no other use than as a roofing material, so what cannot be used is left as waste. This contrasts with, say, a limestone quarry where the material not used for building stone can be crushed and used for roads or cement.

□ (below) There can be considerable environmental damage from quarrying, and it can conflict with other ways of using the land, such as here in the Lake District National Park, England.

□ (above) Local quarries are common all over the developing world. In such places the poorest people are often forced to do hard work such as rock-breaking to earn a living.

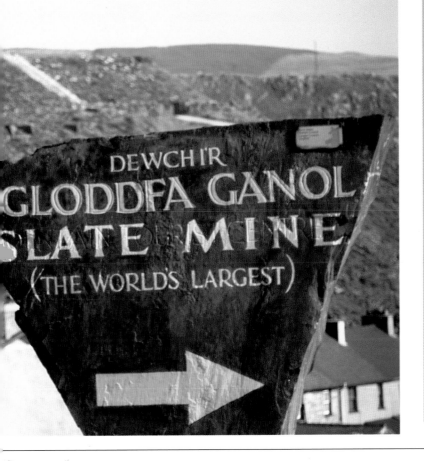

## New super-quarries

Modern quarry owners want to use very large machines, because these can work most economically. But large machines can only work in very large quarries, so quarry owners must make their sites as large as possible.

In some parts of the world, such as Europe, where most land is built up, it is becoming very difficult to find places for new large quarries. People do not want quarries near their homes.

But if fewer very large quarries, that is, super-quarries, are used, then many smaller quarries will not be needed. Only about six to ten super-quarries could, for example, supply rock for the whole of Europe.

However, with fewer quarries, the average distance between quarries and customer will increase, so a cheap way of moving the rock must be found. Because large ships are the cheapest way to move material, the new quarries are most likely to be developed in remote sites on the edge of Europe – hard rock areas like northwestern Scotland or Norway – by the sea.

The scale of these quarries will be immense. Effectively, owners are suggesting that they buy the land that makes up a whole mountain by the sea, that they build a harbour that can take large ships, and that huge machines then be set to blasting the mountain, crushing the rock and loading it onto ships. The rock will then be carried by ship, at low cost, to ports throughout Europe, and by road to the customers.

rivers, ice and the sea. Collecting stone from these areas is preferable to quarrying stone. However, gravel and sand deposits are often just a few metres deep. This means that in collecting these natural aggregates the quarrying industry soon uses up large areas of land.

The coasts contain by far the largest amount of aggregate, in the form of beaches and sand banks in shallow coastal waters. However, there is often a major difficulty with their use. Beaches and sand banks play a vital role in protecting the coastline from the pounding of storm waves. When they are quarried, coasts quickly retreat inland, putting coastal homes in danger.

On the other hand, removing sand banks near harbours is useful. Navigation channels must be kept open by dredging material from the sea bed. Sometimes this material can be used for construction.

There are also some regions where it is safe to dredge at sea. These are in places where the waves and currents naturally produce sand banks. By understanding how nature moves material around shores, it is possible to find areas that can be used without putting shorelines at risk.

> River action, coastal waves and wind naturally sort materials into similar sizes. It is therefore much easier to use these materials than to crush and sort rock. However, it puts great pressure on parts of the landscape like river floodplains and beaches.

## Quarrying for sand and gravel

Working the landscape for natural aggregates saves on the cost of blasting and crushing rock. All that has to be done is to remove the unwanted soil (overburden), then the materials can simply be excavated. In many cases the materials have been sorted naturally, so relatively little grading is needed. This makes such sites particularly attractive to the construction industry, because they can sell the material at a higher profit.

The main sources of material, rivers, old glacier deposits and the sea, are shown on this page.

### 1. Rivers (below)

Rivers carry a wide range of materials which they deposit in their channels. As a river moves about over its floodplain, this material is spread out as sheets. It is often possible, therefore to open up a quarry and scoop out a range of material from a single site. The gravels and sands are usually deposited in layers, making the sorting process even easier.

## 2. Glacial deposits (left)

The useful materials from old glacier deposits were mostly laid down by running water as the ice melted at the end of the Ice Age.

As ice sheets and glaciers melt, they form rivers that dig into glacial debris (sometimes called boulder clay). The huge amounts of readily moved material are sorted by fast-flowing rivers. The gravels are left closest to the ice, sands farther downstream and clays farther away still.

The beds of rivers flowing down below the ice (eskers) contain winding ridges of gravels and sands.

All areas that were covered with ice during the last ice age may contain deposits of these materials.

## 3. Beaches, bars and barriers (below)

Coastal sand and gravel often come from eroding cliffs. From these sources waves and currents move the sand and gravel along the beaches (by a process called longshore drift). Finally the material is washed offshore where it collects as a sandbank or bar.

Sand and gravel are best collected where nature has deposited them, because this will cause the least difficulty for people living along the coast.

In the past this advice has not been followed and some coastal areas have been stripped of their offshore deposits. As a result, coastal settlements have had to build expensive sea walls, while the smallest have been abandoned completely, as shown below in Hallsands, Devon, England.

# Chapter 4

# Minerals and the environment

As people exploit resources, they change the environment. They may dig huge pits, leave piles of rock-spoil, pollute rivers, leave bare ground where there was once forest or drown whole valleys.

It is impossible to leave the landscape untouched, but it is possible to treat the land with care and to repair the damage caused. Conserving the land is a responsibility that comes with getting resources. Companies must make sure they have funds to put the landscape right when they leave a site. Where this has not been thought about and where conservation has not been planned, the landscape has often remained scarred.

Perhaps if the Earth were a dry dusty place like Mars, digging holes here and there would not matter. But the Earth nurtures life that occupies no more than a thin 'film' on the surface. By making use of resources, our scratching on the surface can have devastating effects on plants, wild animals and on ourselves. This is why we need to look at how using the world's resources can affect the environment.

❐ (left) Resources have to be exploited where they occur. But when the site is no longer useful, the land must be restored. If the site is dry, the holes often make good sites for dumping rubbish (called landfill) which can then be covered over with a layer of soil. Otherwise they can be used to make recreational lakes or even refuges for wildlife, if they are adapted with care. However, when entire mountains are destroyed, as here in the Rocky Mountains, USA, the problem is more difficult.

# Mining and quarrying

As we have seen in earlier chapters, there are many types of resource. Each of the main types, rock, timber and water, affects the landscape in its own way and brings its own special problems.

Mining and quarrying involve collecting large amounts of material from the ground. The stages are:

☛ clearing a space for the mine or quarry;

☛ building roads, etc., to get the material from the site;

☛ building processing machines on-site;

☛ opening up the ground on the surface or digging shafts;

☛ dealing with the mixture of resource and waste that is produced;

☛ coping with wastewater that has to be drained from the site;

☛ reclaiming the site after the resources have been used.

Clearly, many problems are involved at each stage.

Mines and quarries use large amounts of land, even if they are mining underground. The material that has been mined or quarried is not usually carried away immediately; it has to be stored until it can be processed or collected. So most sites have large stockpiles of material.

**Excavations that remain dry when they are abandoned can be filled with waste and covered with soil and vegetation.**

More space is needed for the waste rock that is usually produced, and yet more space for the roads, railway lines, canals and buildings that may have to be constructed.

A stockpile of mined minerals can cause immediate problems to the environment, and not simply because it is ugly. Stockpiles are exposed concentrated mineral. When rain falls on the material, the two react. As the water drains through the stockpile it may become

# Reclaiming dry ground

Reclaiming land is costly and difficult, but more and more countries are making companies clear up the mess they leave. In a modern landscape, you may find hills where once there were none. These hills are actually huge piles of spoil, created during the working of the mine or quarry, which have been covered with soil.

One of the main problems of land reclamation was not, however, making the landscape more attractive, but making waste materials safe. In 1966, a pile of coal-spoil that had been stored on a high ridge overlooking the small town of Aberfan in South Wales, became saturated with water and collapsed. The slurry of materials flowed down the hillside and destroyed a school and some other buildings, killing 170 people including 144 schoolchildren.

The disaster prompted the British government (and others) to make laws requiring spoil tips to be made safe. The laws have been adopted in many other countries as well. The effect was dramatic, and nowhere do you now see the tall spoil tips of the past.

But the tragedy has been turned into something good. Because the spoil cannot be piled up high, but must be spread out, it can be turned into farmland, forest or recreational land in a way that was not possible before.

Reclaiming surface-mined areas is easier in places where there is enough rainfall to allow vegetation to grow. It is much more difficult in dry areas, such as the western United States, and Australia or cold areas such as arctic Canada. For these, no solution has yet been found.

❑ (above) Reclamation of spoiled areas is especially important in small places like the Hawaiian islands. Reforesting and reuse of land for recreation might be best for the quarry shown here.

❐ (above) A mine workings in a forested area is being carefully restored in stages. In this picture you can see the area of active workings, and how the land is reclaimed. The material is piled up and then graded (smoothed down) to make stable slopes that blend in with the landscape. Soil is then spread over the rock waste, and eventually the soil is planted with grass or trees and used as productive forest or farmland.

❐ (left) Huge areas of the island of Phuket, Thailand, were stripped away as part of tin mining. At least part of these have now been recovered as a golf course.

❐ (right) Landfill. People create an enormous amount of waste, and one of the biggest problems is how to dispose of it. A large hole left after mining or quarrying could be filled with this waste material, provided the rock is watertight. If it is not, there is a danger that rainwater seeping through the waste buried in the hole will contaminate water supplies.

Unfortunately, many sites are not watertight, so most holes created by mining resources cannot be filled this way.

contaminated with minerals that can be harmful to the environment if present in large quantities. It is therefore very important to collect the water from the sites (and also the water drained from underground workings) and make sure that they are cleaned.

Only a small number of flooded sites can be used because of the danger that the water might become contaminated.

As the mine or quarry grows, the piles of waste rock become larger and space has to be found for it. In the case of stone this can be on a huge scale. For example, in slate quarries 19 tonnes of rock may be wasted for every 1 tonne of roofing slate that can be sold. In underground

□ (below) This area has just been abandoned. In its present state it does not make a useful recreation site, but by skilfully remodelling some of the walls between the lakes it can be made more attractive.

## Reclaiming wet ground

The rocks beneath every landscape contain water which often seeps from one layer to another. Because this water is under pressure, people can dig wells for a permanent and easily accessible water supply. When a well is dug, water is forced from the surrounding rock into the well. When water is taken from a well, more seeps in to take its place. If no one used the well, the water level would rise until it balanced the pressure of water in the rocks.

When quarries or mines are opened in a landscape, they act like wells on a grand scale. Water seeps into the workings and can make mining and quarrying impossible. The water must continually be pumped away.

The cost of pumping is high, and although this can be covered when the resource is being mined or quarried, as soon as the workings are abandoned the pumping stops and water fills the workings until it reaches a stable level. It is not safe to use a flood-prone excavation for landfill, but if the excavation is very deep it is also unsafe to use it for recreation.

The easiest holes to use are shallow pits in river floodplains that have been worked for sand and gravel. The deep pits created when excavating for minerals such as copper, or stone such as granite, are much harder to use, and represent a problem for which, as yet, there is no answer.

❐ (left, below and right) Because aggregates are needed for housing, suburbs and quarries are often close together (picture at left). On a floodplain the quarry can leave large shallow holes which fill with water as they are abandoned. These make good recreational sites for a number of uses. In the best schemes, the quarries are separated out into zones, each based on a former quarry pit, now renamed a lake. One lake might be used for water sports, another for sailing, a third for fishing and a fourth left without a use for wildlife and wildlife watchers (picture below). In this way a potential eyesore can be made into an attractive landscape feature. Many such areas are then designated as Country Parks, a replanting scheme begun and the parks supervised by wardens. Such a scheme can be implemented on the abandoned workings shown in the middleground of the picture on the right even while there are working areas nearby.

workings, the spoil is often packed back into exhausted parts of the workings. In surface mines and quarries the material is pushed to the worked-out part of the site. But often there remains a surplus of material that must be stored above ground, usually forming large mounds.

# When the land is abandoned

When a mine or quarry is exhausted, a whole series of new problems arises. Again, this affects both underground and surface workings. There is little that can be done to fill in underground workings, and they are normally simply abandoned. However, the land above may begin to subside and collapse into the old workings. This means that building on the land will be dangerous for many years.

But the real problem with surface mines and quarries is what to do with the large hole that has been created. It is rarely possible to fill in any but the smallest holes. In some cases, if they are close to centres of population, the hole can be filled with rubbish (landfill) from nearby communities. However, the holes may often be far from convenient places, and this option is not open.

Some holes will naturally fill with water. They cannot be used for storing garbage because the garbage will react with the water and contamination will eventually reach rivers and drinking water supplies. For this reason the best use to make of water-filled sites (unless they are dangerously deep) is to landscape them as lakes and recreation sites.

In the past, less care was taken to avoid polluting the land with mining wastes. As a result, some places can no longer support life. It is almost impossible to reclaim such spoiled areas, so they will remain as scars for centuries.

## Toxic mine waste

Mining can cause all manner of problems, but one of the most serious is the problem of mine waste. Waste is created as people search for concentrated deposits of the minerals they want, discarding other minerals on waste heaps. For example, when people searched for gold in the past, they often found deposits of lead. At that time these deposits were too small to be mined, so they dumped them on the landscape. The lead concentration of these piles is far too high for any plants to grow, and each time it rains some of the lead reacts with the water and eventually finds it way to rivers – and possibly to the drinking supplies of people a long way from the spoil.

Another example of dangerous waste is pyrite (iron sulphide). When dumped on the ground, it reacts with oxygen and water to form sulphuric acid. As a result, acid continually seeps into the ground and reaches nearby water supplies. Uncontrolled dumping of toxic (life-threatening) waste is probably one of the most serious hazards produced by mining.

In the United States, for example, pollution from old mines seeping into rivers has polluted about 16,000 km of rivers, while mining creates nearly 4 billion tonnes of further waste each year.

(above and below) This landscape has been ruined by careless mining during a rush to supply minerals for industry. Enormous scientific effort is now being applied to discover ways of neutralising the toxic waste.

(below left and above) Mine tailings, or waste, and polluted mine water cause major problems in all countries. Usually such sites are seriously polluted with heavy metals and they are easy to spot because nothing grows on them. Reclaiming toxic sites is extremely difficult and costly.

# Chapter 5

# Timber

Timber is a renewable resource: cut a tree down and another will, in time, grow in its place. Timber is also a very versatile material that can be made into anything from paper to chemicals.

But people have taken forests for granted, and now trees are less plentiful than they once were. In some places, such as the forests of conifers that grow in cool climates, the loss of timber has already caused problems, and now great replanting schemes are underway. In many tropical countries, logging is still happening at a frightening pace, with few signs of replanting.

Wood has been a favourite resource throughout mankind's existence. This is because wood has so many useful properties. For example, it is waterproof, it can keep out cold or heat, it can easily be cut into a wide variety of shapes, and cut pieces can be cut again for new uses. Many kinds of wood stand up well to the weather and even outlast buildings made of concrete or stone. Wood is also a source of fuel.

Although there are thousands of species of trees, all can be grouped as either hardwoods or softwoods. Most hardwoods come from trees with broad leaves, such as oaks and beeches or teak.

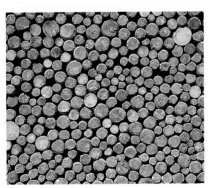

❐ (left) We demand enormous supplies of timber and forests must be cut down to supply it. In general large trees make planks for lumber; small logs (right) are used for posts.

Such trees grow slowly and put on a ring of very dense wood each year. Most softwoods are conifers. These trees grow more quickly.

Most hardwoods are much stronger and far less prone to rotting than softwoods. This is one reason hardwoods such have traditionally been used to make the main support timbers for buildings.

Timber has to be harvested from places that are easy to reach.

However, although many conifers are soft and rot quickly, there are exceptions, such as the cedar, which is used to make roofing materials and the weatherboarding of many wooden houses.

Some wood is prized just for the beauty of its grain. Yew and rosewood timber have a fine grain, while the strange bulbous growths on trees like maples and redwoods – known as burl – have a swirling grain that can give a decorative finish.

❐ (right) Traditional logging of softwoods in Canada. The trees were cut in winter and organised into loads that could be pulled by horses. The logs were hauled out in deep snow, which made them easier to haul, and taken to frozen rivers. In the spring, as the rivers melted, the logs floated down to sawmills.

This system of logging depended on natural waterways, and protected land away from the rivers. The arrival of the railway and logging trucks changed that and made all forests vulnerable.

❐ (below) Modern mechanised handling.

## Harvesting timber

The first stage of logging is to cut down selected trees with a chain saw. Most large trees are still felled by people using portable chain saws, although special machines do exist that will grip small trees, cut them off at the base, strip off the branches and bark and then cut the logs to size – all in one operation that takes just a few seconds.

Once the trees have been felled and the branches cut off, the main trunks are hauled from the forest and transported to their market. Traditionally animals hauled the logs to the river where they were thrown in and floated downstream. But the vast majority of logs are now hauled by tractor, loaded onto trucks and transported by road. On steep slopes, the trees are brought to roadways on cables strung high above the ground.

In some parts of the world, the climate makes short hauling easier at some times in the year. In regions that receive heavy snowfall, such as in Canada or Scandinavia, most trees are cut in winter when the snow makes hauling logs much easier.

Where it is possible, the logs are still hauled onto frozen rivers and floated to sawmills when the rivers melt in spring. The trouble with this system is that the trees can only be harvested at one time of the year. In addition, many of the areas close to the rivers have been logged-out.

❐ (right) Trees are felled over an entire area to make it possible for the logs to be moved by large machines. In this picture you see the trees felled and the branches stripped away. The trunks are now being removed by truck.

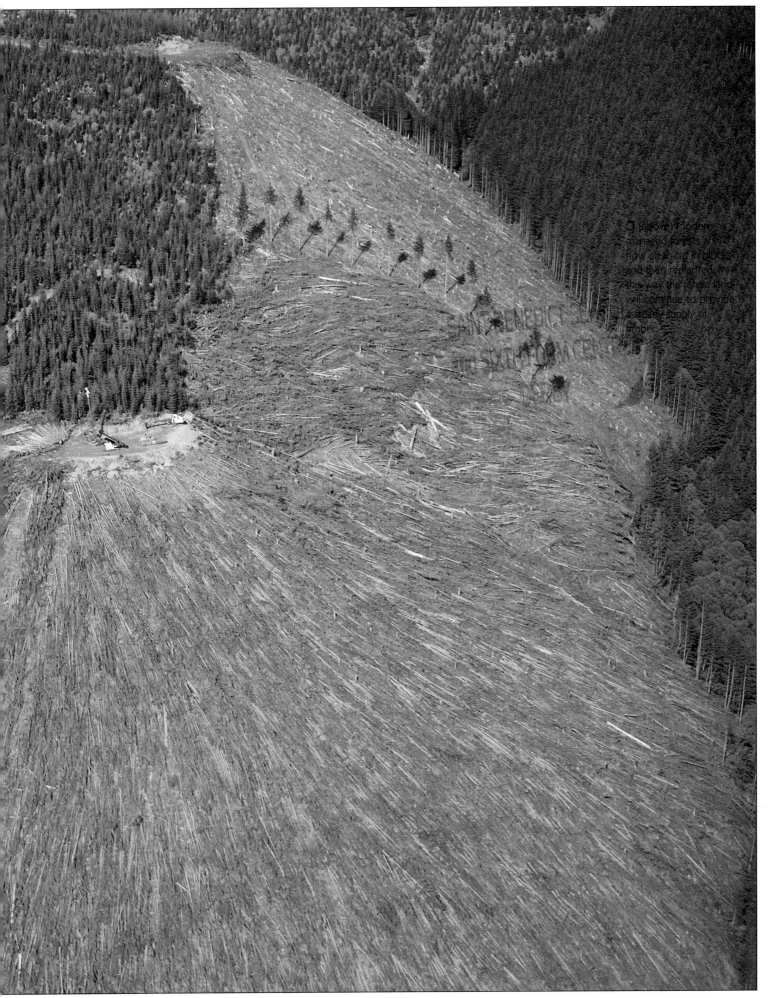

(above) Modern managed forests are now clear-cut in blocks and then replanted. In this way the forest land will continue to provide a steady supply of timber.

# The uses of timber

Each species of tree has its own special characteristics that make it suitable for some uses and less suitable for others. The main uses of timber are for lumber, pulp and paper, chemicals to make materials such as resins and artificial fibres like rayon, and for posts and fuel.

The nature of the trees in a forest will affect the kind of uses that the wood can be put to and the price the tree will fetch. For example, if the trees are smaller than about 20 cm across

Timber was one of the few materials that our early ancestors could work with. It is flexible, strong, a good insulator, cheap and it does not rot quickly. Thus, it is still a favoured material.

and about 2-3 m long, then they cannot be sawn up into useful planks for lumber. If a tree is to be used for making the surface layer (veneer) of furniture, then it must have a pronounced and attractive pattern and must be as free from knots as possible.

But tall thin straight trunks that may not make good lumber may be just right for pit props or telegraph poles. And softwood trees that are unsuited for any timber use can be made into sawdust and used as pulp for making paper.

Softwoods are widely used for making lumber, because the wood is far easier to cut than hardwood. However it must then be treated with a preservative if it is to be used in a place exposed to the weather. Most softwood forests grow in cool climates, such as in the mountains of the United States, Canada, Scandinavia, Russia, Australia, New Zealand, Chile and Japan.

## Lumber

Lumber is the name for prepared wood, including planks, sheets, posts and veneers.

Most of the world's lumber comes from just two areas: nearly a third from Russia and about a fifth from North America. Much of the rest comes from tropical countries. Both of the major areas have vast conifer forests that yield softwoods used to make building materials; tropical lands yield hardwoods used to make furniture and floorboards.

## Using logs

1. Logs are delivered to the mills by truck and rail, and are stockpiled. They are sprayed during storage to prevent fire risk and damage by wood-boring insects.
2. The bark is stripped off the logs which are then cut into thick sheets. Some of these sheets will be used directly for such things as table tops, but most will be cut again into long strips of standard sizes.
3. The sized wood still contains a large amount of water and unless it is dried will be unsuitable for construction. Traditionally, timber was stacked up and left to dry naturally over the years. However, the demand for quick turnaround of timber has meant that modern timber is dried quickly in heated ovens known as kilns.
4. Sawdust, chips and other waste materials are often bonded together with glues to make chipboard and other particle boards. These are then used to make inexpensive furniture.

(above) Where it is possible, logs are still brought to the sawmill by river and then floated into the mill. In the past, most forests were harvested close to rivers but not replanted, so today only a few areas can supply logs for floating. Expensive trucking systems are used instead.

Power station and cogeneration plant burns wood waste to generate power for the mills and houses in the nearby town

Drying kilns

Saw mills

Ponds for storing timber brought down the river in spring

(right) Timber is a heavy, bulky material; most sawmills are therefore close to the forests that supply them, like this one in northern California.

Once the logs have been made into lumber (planks and other shapes of timber) they are worth more and can be transported farther while still making a profit.

The mill has to be adapted to use the waste material for a variety of purposes, such as making chipboard.

Stored timber

River transports some logs by flotation

# Revolutions in forest use

People naturally turned to timber as the easiest source of building materials and for fuel. Hewing trees to make log cabins was a very crude and wasteful way of using timber, and most societies soon developed skills in sawing logs into planks.

As demand grew, hand sawing was replaced by saw mills. Some saw mills were operated by wind power (as in The Netherlands) but the majority were powered by running water. Most saw mills were thus built next to a river in an area surrounded by a forest that provided the raw materials.

The main challenge of modern forestry is to make sure that forests are replanted so that the resource does not run out. There was not enough replanting in the past and this is causing problems today. It may take half a century to put the situation right.

At first, most saw mills were small and family-owned. However, during the 19th century, as the Industrial Revolution developed and water power was replaced by steam, mills became larger and family mills became company mills.

The bigger mills using steam for power did not need to be sited near fast-flowing water to turn the waterwheel. Instead they could be developed on navigable rivers. This meant that logs could be floated down-river to them, and the finished lumber could be sent out by ship.

The timber industry was not concerned at this time with conservation. Areas would be logged-out and new mills opened in unused forest. In this way, for example, saw mills moved across the United States along with the advance of farmland. It began in the 17th century in the colonies of the northeast,

## Managing forest resources

Forestry is the practice of managing forests. Each type of forest is unique and so needs unique management. In managed forests, at least as much forest grows as is harvested. Wood from such managed forests was used to make the paper for this book.

But because in the past far less attention was paid to forest management, the world's forests stocks need to be increased. There has been great success with this in the last few decades in most industrial countries. The largest replanted area in the world is in the state of Louisiana in the United States, where over 24,000 ha. of pine have been replanted since the 1930s.

Management of forests also requires careful cutting systems. Ideally, only the larger trees should be logged from a natural forest. This gives younger trees the chance to grow up and set seed, thus creating more seedlings for future trees.

But the advent of large machines has made this practice difficult. As a result, many forests are cut in blocks or patches, with all trees cleared away and replanted with seedlings grown in nurseries.

The disadvantage of patch cutting is that it leaves unpleasant bare areas between harvesting and the time the new trees start growing. It also gives rise to even stands of trees that grow closely together and that do not provide a natural environment for wildlife.

Increasingly, forests are also seen as a resource for recreation, so management has to cater not only for the needs of the timber industry, but also for wildlife and people. It is a difficult balance to achieve.

□ (right) This is a typical modern replanting scheme. A large block of forest has been clear cut, but the stumps are not removed. In this way the land is disturbed as little as possible. Small seedlings, grown in a nursery, are planted, and the stumps allowed to rot and fertilise the new trees. Then the forest is left to grow until it is ready for harvesting again.

□ (left) It has been common practice to plant trees close together so they will grow straight and with fewer branches (and therefore fewer knots). This kind of planting however, is not very good for the environment.

□ (left and above) For many generations, people harvested trees without planting new ones. The supply seemed endless, and successfully cutting down the forest giants, such as the 100 m tall redwood trees shown here, was a reason for celebration.

However, the old wood forests have become scarce, and all timber companies now have major replanting schemes to ensure they do not run out of resources.

# Logging and land erosion

Timber is a natural material, but taking away the trees can do much harm to the environment. This is because of the way that the land is often logged.

Like all other industries that deal with materials in bulk, the lumber industry tries to use big machines so that it can keep its costs as low as possible. But big machines can only work efficiently if they can clear whole areas of a forest at the same time. When they clear a naturally grown forest, they cut down all the trees, young and old alike. At the same time the movement of the machines over the soft ground compacts the surface soil.

The next time rain falls the problem becomes clear: with no leaves or soft ground to absorb the rain, water runs over the surface and gets to the rivers much more quickly than normal. This in turn causes rivers to flood more often.

At the same time, water flowing over the bare surface of the cleared plot picks up soil that has taken tens of thousands of years to develop and carries it away. It enters rivers, turning them brown, polluting water supplies and making it harder to use the rivers for drinking water.

Some of the silt settles out on the river beds, raising them up, shrinking the river channel and making rivers more likely to flood in heavy rainfall. The silt finally accumulates in the sluggish waters near the sea, making it difficult for boats to navigate.

moved south in the 18th century and west into the area around the Great Lakes during the 19th century. A similar pattern occurred in Canada.

Today the largest areas of forest are now in the West, in the states of Oregon, Washington and California. In Canada the best logging areas are also in the west, in British Columbia. In countries such as Britain, however, there was a much more serious crisis developing. No western European country had huge, untapped forests like those in North America, Scandinavia or Siberian Russia.

> Trees are important as a supply of timber and fuelwood. But they also help prevent flooding, drought, and soil loss, and they even affect the world's climate. All this needs to be taken into account when managing this priceless resource.

The forests had long been logged-out, and only the highland regions kept any forests. So, western Europe began to import timber, providing profits to forested countries, but causing them to be deforested at an ever-increasing rate.

World War 1 convinced all countries that timber was one of the most valuable resources and, for example, in Britain the Forestry Commission was set up to begin to replant areas of land. In the United States a system of National Forests were set up as reserves for similar reasons.

Timber is not now used widely for fuel in industrial countries because supplies of timber are scarce enough to keep prices high.

## Timber in the tropics

In industrial countries, the cost of timber is high, but it has traditionally been an inexpensive resource in the developing world. Here, up to nine-tenths of all timber is used as fuel and burned in hearths for cooking and heating.

People are very particular about their use of trees for cooking: some woods are smoky and burn at a low temperature, while others burn with little smoke and at a higher temperature. Most deciduous trees in the tropics yield hardwood, which burns slowly at a high temperature and is good for fires. Most evergreen trees are softwoods and are more often cut for timber.

Logging has increased rapidly in recent decades due to the demand for timber in the industrial world. Japan, in particular, has paid high prices for timber with good grain, thus making it even more attractive for companies to log-out forests.

❏ (above) In some developing countries there is great pressure on forest resources for a number of reasons. The timber will fetch high prices on the world market, and, because many people in developing countries are poor, this is an attractive way to make a living.

But the land occupied by trees is also land that could be used for farming, and huge areas have been cleared for planting.

People in cool climates also clear forests for farmland, but in these areas soils store more nourishment than in tropical climates. So in tropical areas there has been a great and tragic loss of forest resource, with nothing to take its place.

□ (above) Perhaps the most serious problem of all is the way that forests are being cut down in the mountains. Half a century ago this Himalayan valley would have been covered with forests that protected the soil from torrential downpours. Now the trees are gone, and rain rushes to the streams and carries precious soil away, making these regions less and less fertile.

□ (left) As populations grow, and there are more people seeking jobs, the pressure to use more timber also increases. Cheap labour makes it profitable to make furniture for export.

□ (right) Traditional methods of logging relied on harvesting trees one at a time and then using methods of carrying the trees away that did not harm the environment. However, such systems have long been replaced by much less careful methods.

# Chapter 6

# Water resources

The world contains vast water resources, but over 97 per cent is in the form of salt water and four-fifths of the rest is locked up in ice sheets. This means that less than I per cent of the world's water resources occurs as rivers and lakes, and in rocks underground. Of this, the vast majority – some 95 per cent – is held in soil and rocks.

The world's fresh water supplies are not spread evenly among the places where people live, so in general there is a surplus of water in places with low population, and severe shortages where the population is high.

To try to make the best use of the world's fresh water resources, water is taken from rivers and lakes, held behind dams and moved vast distances by canal. And wherever possible water is taken from underground through wells and pumps.

The Earth's water resources are provided by the constant movement of moisture between the oceans and the atmosphere, called the water cycle. The rain that falls first makes the ground vegetation (or roofs and streets) wet. Afterward the water seeps into the ground or, in the case of built-up areas, runs into drains.

❐ (left) Large areas of land have been flooded to make way for reservoirs in order to meet the ever-growing demand for water.

The water that reaches the soil is held in small gaps called pores. Once they are full surplus water moves through the soil and into pores in the underlying rock. Some rocks have enormous networks of connecting pores. These are called water-bearing rocks, or aquifers, and their water can be tapped using wells and pumps.

> A reliable supply of clean water is an absolute necessity. Thus, we have to store and purify water carefully.

Not all of the water that seeps into soils will seep into rivers. Much of it will be lost back to the air, or sucked from the soil by plant roots and transpired through their leaves.

The water moving through the soils and rocks feeds springs and supplies water to the rivers through the bed and banks.

Rivers receive between a third and two-thirds of their water from rocks and soils, and almost all of the rest as short bursts of high water when rainfall runs over the soil surface during storms. This means that, between storms, people depend on seepage of water from soils and rocks to provide the rivers that give them their supplies of drinking and irrigation water, or they depend on the water stored in the rock to keep wells filled.

# An unevenly spread resource

On average about 40,000 cubic kilometres of water flow down the world's rivers each year. This huge volume of water is a resource that people can use. Clearly it would be helpful if rain fell evenly on every part of the Earth, but of course this is not the case. A fifth of it flows down the Amazon River in South America alone, while virtually none of it flows through the third of the world's land surface that is desert.

The pattern of rainfall throughout the year is also vary variable. Rain tends to fall in isolated storms, or in rainy seasons, separated by fine,

# Water treatment and home supply

Water occurs in rivers and lakes, as well as underground. It has to be supplied to industry, farms and homes through complicated networks of pipes and canals.

Water supply is not just a matter of providing the amount of water that is demanded. Water supply concerns recycling; four-fifths of the water used is not consumed and must be returned for further use. Water must also be supplied at the right quality. No one would, for example, choose to drink water directly from a river. Between the river and the taps we use for drinking, lies a complex purification system.

❑ (below) Water treatment is an essential part of any water supply system. Many natural substances and organisms are found in all rivers and lakes, and tiny particles (sediment) are suspended in water. The treatment plant has to kill the organisms and remove the sediment.

The degree of treatment depends on the intended consumer. Water supplied to farms for irrigation and factories for cooling systems may need no treatment, whereas water supplied for home use must be fully treated.

A treatment works consists of a number of settling pools and filtration beds. Part of the treatment in these beds is simply to filter out the sediment, but part is a chemical process (such as chlorination) designed to disinfect the water, and part of it is biological, where microbes are used to digest some of the waste materials.

(left) Water is supplied to homes, factories and offices through rivers and aqueducts in the countryside and through trunk pipes inside the city. City supply pipes are usually arranged in great loops so that water can reach any point from two directions. This is of great value if there is a leak in the system and one section has to be shut down.

Along the trunk pipes there are many branches which serve different regions. From these branches, water runs under streets through pipes that feed to each consumer.

(above) Water flowing to a treatment works in the Ruhr industrial region of Germany. The amount of purification that has to be achieved is obvious.

(above) Some cities need more water than their local reservoirs, rivers and aquifers can provide. These cities are connected to distant rivers and reservoirs by aqueducts, such as those that carry water from the Colorado River to Los Angeles, California.

rainless spells. On some occasions the rain will fall from storms that are so heavy there is no chance for the rain to seep into the soils. When this happens the rain will simply flow over the surface, increasing the chance of floods. On other occasions rain may be far less than normal, thus causing a drought when rivers may dry up.

# Supply and demand

People use water in very different ways. This is shown by the world's biggest users of water – the United States, the Commonwealth of Independent States (CIS, formerly the USSR), India and China –

> It is getting harder and harder to find new supplies of water, so ways have to be found to use water more efficiently.

who use about 45 per cent of the world's total supply. However, they use it for very different reasons. The United States uses far more water per person than any other country, nearly 60 per cent of which goes to industry and around 33 per cent for irrigation. About 8 per cent is used for homes. By contrast, the CIS uses half of its water for irrigation and 45 per cent for industry, with only 3 per cent for homes. India and China use about 95 per cent of their water for irrigation, while people consume only 1 to 2 per cent.

## Water supply and the environment

Because water is such a critical resource, people are prepared to make the storage of water a very high priority. As a result there can be a conflict between water supply and the environment. Many conflicts arise partly because people do not use water carefully, since it is still a cheap resource.

The major concerns over water include: ruining vast areas of land due to poor irrigation of farmland; large dams flooding vast amounts of land; controlling of natural rivers to the extent that they no longer support their original wildlife; and polluting waterways with poor-quality water.

### Problems of large dams

Thousands of large dams have been built across the world. In some developing world countries the idea that the country could have the world's biggest dam or largest reservoir is attractive to politicians. The money to pay for such schemes comes from international funds, and so for poor countries this makes big schemes doubly attractive.

But big dams and huge reservoirs are often much more costly than many small dams that would have supplied the same amount of water. Big dams also create reservoirs that may be hundreds of kilometres long. They may store water, but they may also ruin other resources, such as land for farming and forests.

Reservoirs have to be connected to the consumers: the more scattered the reservoirs, the shorter the pipe network and the easier it is to keep it in working order. Because there are few places that are suitable for large dams, water may have to be transferred large distances, adding yet more to the costs and increasing the chances of the supply failing.

❒ (above) A dam built to store water has flooded the valley behind.
❒ (opposite page, bottom picture) These circular fields only flourish because water is pumped from underground and then sprayed onto the crops. Otherwise the land would only support rough grazing (pictures at top of page).
❒ (left) The need for fresh water can upset environments far away. This picture of Mono Lake, California, shows tide lines where the water level has fallen as water is taken from the region to supply Los Angeles, hundreds of kilometres away. Recent agreements will now halt the fall in water level, in contrast to the loss of water to the Aral Sea in Uzbekistan, once the world's fourth largest inland sea. The Aral Sea has shrunk to half its size in 20 years as rivers have been diverted for irrigation. The loss of the Aral Sea is regarded as one of the world's greatest environmental disasters.

## Mining groundwater

Because people in dry areas or highly populated areas are anxious to get as much water from the rocks as possible, they risk overpumping the groundwater. This can make the underground rocks settle and cause the ground to subside. Some areas of California's San Joaquin Valley have sunk over 10 m in the last 50 years as the result of taking too much underground water for irrigation.

## Use of and problems with groundwater

Much of the water we use comes from underground. But using groundwater raises problems. Water underground moves slowly over many years, during which time chemical reactions occur between the rocks and the water. This is what makes some water 'hard'. But far more serious are the salts that water can pick up.

Groundwater is sometimes salty – brackish – and is unsuitable for people to drink. Some animals, however, can drink it. Much of the water of Australia's Great Artesian Basin – the world's biggest aquifer – is slightly brackish but still suitable for animals. Wind pumps bring it to the surface to provide water in the dry outback.

There are 250 million ha. of irrigated farmland, 17 per cent of the world's total farmland. It is dangerous to use brackish groundwater for irrigation. The salts in the water can easily build up in the soils, making the soil toxic to plants and preventing new growth. This is called salinisation. To stop salts building up, the water must be drained out of the soils and flushed away downstream.

Salinisation is found all over the world. The Middle East, one of the earliest irrigation areas and once one of the most productive, now has only poor crops. In the Indus Valley of Pakistan, the world's largest irrigation scheme, millions of hectares are affected by salinisation, amounting to 10 per cent of all of its farmland. Large areas of Australia are similarly affected and have had to be abandoned. In all about a third of the world's irrigated cropland has salinisation problems.

Despite the various ways that people use water, the natural pattern of water flow in rivers does not match their needs very closely. People need water throughout the year, but rainfall usually varies with the seasons. So people have to look for methods to match the irregular supply from rainfall with their more or less constant needs and to make sure their needs do not outstrip the supply!

If we added up all of the water that people actually used, the total would be more than actually flows in the rivers. However, people do not consume all of the water they use. This seemingly impossible remark can be explained with some examples. In the home people use large amounts of water for flushing toilets, for baths and for cooking and cleaning. But this water is used then returned (via treatment plants) to rivers. As a result the loss to the rivers is very small. Similarly, power stations use very large amounts of water for cooling, but 97 per cent of it is returned to rivers.

On the other hand, there are some uses of water where much of it is lost to the air and never returns to rivers. The biggest of these uses is irrigating crops. Much of the water is used by plants that evaporate the water back into the atmosphere. So when we think about the need for water, we have to take into account water that is recycled as well as water that is consumed.

There are other considerations as well. For example, if we were to use all of the water in a river, it would dry up, killing the wildlife and making navigation impossible. It would also concentrate the pollution in the water, leading to health hazards. So we simply cannot take as much as we want: some of the water that is in a river has to remain there.

> We all understand the need for clean water, but in many countries it has not yet been possible to provide it.

## Water resources in the developing world

Water is vital, yet it is not easily available in two-thirds of the world. For the unlucky majority, water has to be fetched and carried and much is not safe to drink.

The problem in developing world countries is made more severe by the rapidly rising populations and the lack of money to build suitable supplies.

Many water supplies are contaminated by poor sanitation, especially in the slum areas of cities. Providing clean, fresh water has to be one of the world's top priorities, and to achieve this people must begin to use the land differently, to build safe latrines and to keep human water supplies separate from those used by animals.

❐ (above and right) Everyone appreciates the need for clean water. Many people are prepared to carry water from public supplies even though they may live many kilometres away.

❐ (below) People in remote areas with a long dry season can help themselves by storing rainwater from their own roofs. This stone jar is designed to help a family over a couple of months at the end of the dry season when rivers all run dry. There are hundreds of thousands of such jars all over Africa. Could you survive on such a small amount of water?

❐ (above) Unless people can store water during the dry season they may be in serious trouble. This picture shows a person collecting water from the bottom of a dried-up river bed.

❐ (below) Few city people in the developing world have their own water supply. Most have to make use of standpipes set up among their communities.

It is believed that about 10,000 cubic kilometres of water must remain in rivers for these purposes, no matter what the demand. What we can use is only the 'surplus': 30,000 cubic kilometres. But because the flow of water is also unreliable and varies over the year, the most reasonable amount of water that we could take from rivers is about 10 per cent of the total, about 3000 cubic kilometres a year.

After recycling water, people take about 2500 cubic kilometres a day from the world's rivers and aquifers, just about four-fifths of the world's available freshwater supply. But as the population of the world grows, and as people have more need for water, the demand is sure to rise.

It will probably rise very little in the industrial countries because here people are learning how to conserve water. However, in the developing world people already use the bare minimum, and as populations grow, the demand must rise in proportion. It may well be that by the middle of the 21st century the demand will be 20,000 cubic kilometres a year, a figure that just cannot be provided! Indeed, some people believe that it is the shortage of water, not the shortage of food, that may be the world's most critical problem of resources in the next century. Unlike other resources, such as petroleum or grain, it is not easy to share water resources. So a surplus in one country cannot easily be transferred to another. This means that each country has to look out for itself. In some parts of the world this can be a frightening prospect.

❏ (above) Drip feed irrigation in a Californian vineyard. The drip feed directs water to the roots of the plants rather than over the soil. This is a good example of how people have thought of better ways to use water as it becomes more expensive.

❏ (right) Las Vegas is built in a desert. All the water has to be piped from reservoirs or from other, distant, sources. But this resource is not wasted in such things as the city's artificial waterfalls: this one uses recycled water.

# Glossary

## BRONZE AGE

The Bronze Age is the time when bronze (which is a mixture of copper and tin) was used for implements and weapons. It occurs between the Stone Age and the Iron Age.

## DEVELOPING WORLD

Countries where the majority of people still depend on farming for their living, where most wages are low (compared with industrial countries) and where there is a lack of advanced technology such as electricity in every home. There are 125 countries classified by the United Nations as coming into this category, including most of those in Asia, Africa and South America.

## INDUSTRIAL REVOLUTION

The time during the 18th and 19th centuries when the world first saw automatic machines and steam power. Its most common symbol was the factory.

## IRON AGE

The Iron Age is the time when people began to learn how to use iron to make implements and weapons, instead of bronze. It began in the Middle East about 3000 years ago and spread westwards through Europe and eastwards to China in the next 500 years.

## MIDDLE AGES

The Middle Ages is the period between the end of the Roman Empire and the 15th century, a time span of about a thousand years. It is a term that really only applies to European history.

## PLACER DEPOSITS

The heavy minerals, especially metals, that are transported by rivers or waves and become concentrated on a river bed or near the shore. The majority of the world's tin, diamonds, and gold are obtained from placer deposits.

## SEDIMENTARY

Anything connected with the laying down of fine materials in layers due to the action of running water, waves and currents or wind. Sedimentary rocks are therefore layered rocks.

## STONE AGE

The Stone Age is the earliest period during which people learned to make stone tools and weapons. It lasted from about 2.5 million to about 10,000 years ago

# Further reading

This book is one of a series that covers the whole of geography. They may provide you with more information. The series is:

1. **People** of the world, population & migration
2. **Homes** of the world & the way people live
3. The world's **shops** & where they are
4. **Cities** of the world & their future
5. World **transport**, travel & communications
6. **Farms** & the world's food supply

7. World **industry** & making goods
8. The world's **resources** & their exploitation
9. The world's changing **energy** supplies
10. The world's **environments** & conservation
11. World **weather**, climate & climatic change
12. The **Earth** & its changing surface

# Index

World Geography  People of the world, population & migration  Homes of the world & the way people live  The world's shops & where they are  Cities of the world & changing energy supplies  The world's environment & conservation  World weather, climate & climatic change  The Earth & its changing surface  World Geography travel & communications  Farms & the world's food supply  World industry & making goods  The world's resources & their exploitation  The world's changing energy su & migration  Homes of the world & the way people live  The world's shops & where they are  Cities of the world & their future  World transport, travel & communica & conservation  World weather, climate & climatic change  The Earth & its changing surface  World Geography  People of the world, population & migration  Home supply  World industry & making goods  The world's resources & their exploitation  The world's changing energy supplies  The world's environment & conservation live  The world's shops & where they are  Cities of the world & their future  World transport, travel & communications  Farms & the world's food supply  World indust change  The Earth & its changing surface  World Geography  People of the world, population & migration  Homes of the world & the way people live  The world's sho resources & their exploitation  The world's changing energy supplies  The world's environment & conservation  World weather, climate & climatic change  The Earth of the world & their future  World transport, travel & communications  Farms & the world's food supply  World industry & making goods  The world's resources & their Geography  People of the world, population & migration  Homes of the world & the way people live  The world's shops & where they are  Cities of the world & their futu energy supplies  The world's environment & conservation  World weather, climate & climatic change  The Earth & its changing surface  World Geography  People o communications  Farms & the world's food supply  World industry & making goods  The world's resources & their exploitation  The world's changing energy supplies  Th Homes of the world & the way people live  The world's shops & where they are  Cities of the world & their future  World transport, travel & communications  Farms & t World weather, climate & climatic change  The Earth & its changing surface  World Geography  People of the world, population & migration  Homes of the world & industry & making goods  The world's resources & their exploitation  The world's changing energy supplies  The world's environment & conservation  World weathe world's shops & where they are  Cities of the world & their future  World transport, travel & communications  Farms & the world's food supply  World industry & m The Earth & its changing surface  World Geography  People of the world, population & migration  Homes of the world & the way people live  The world's shops & wh & their exploitation  The world's changing energy supplies  The world's environment & conservation  World weather, climate & climatic change  The Earth & its chan & their future  World transport, travel & communications  Farms & the world's food supply  World industry & making goods  The world's resources & their exploitatio People of the world, population & migration  Homes of the world & the way people live  The world's shops & where they are  Cities of the world & their future  World supplies  The world's environment & conservation  World weather, climate & climatic change  The Earth & its changing surface  World Geography  People of the world Farms & the world's food supply  World industry & making goods  The world's resources & their exploitation  The world's changing energy supplies  The world's env of the world & the way people live  The world's shops & where they are  Cities of the world & their future  World transport, travel & communications  Farms & the wo weather, climate & climatic change  The Earth & its changing surface  World Geography  People of the world, population & migration  Homes of the world & the wa & making goods  The world's resources & their exploitation  The world's changing energy supplies  The world's environment & conservation  World weather, climate & where they are  Cities of the world & their future  World transport, travel & communications  Farms & the world's food supply  World industry & making goods & its changing surface  World Geography  People of the world, population & migration  Homes of the world & the way people live  The world's shops & where they are exploitation  The world's changing energy supplies  The world's environment & conservation  World weather, climate & climatic change  The Earth & its changing su future  World transport, travel & communications  Farms & the world's food supply  World industry & making goods  The world's resources & their exploitation  The u of the world, population & migration  Homes of the world & the way people live  The world's shops & where they are  Cities of the world & their future  World transp The world's environment & conservation  World weather, climate & climatic change  The Earth & its changing surface  World Geography  People of the world, popu Farms & the world's food supply  World industry & making goods  The world's resources & their exploitation  The world's changing energy supplies  The world's env of the world & the way people live  The world's shops & where they are  Cities of the world & their future  World transport, travel & communications  Farms & the worl weather, climate & climatic change  The Earth & its changing surface  World Geography  People of the world, population & migration  Homes of the world & the wa & making goods  The world's resources & their exploitation  The world's changing energy supplies  The world's environment & conservation  World weather, climate & where they are  Cities of the world & their future  World transport, travel & communications  Farms & the world's food supply  World industry & making goods & its changing surface  World Geography  People of the world, population & migration  Homes of the world & the way people live  The world's shops & where they ar exploitation  The world's changing energy supplies  The world's environment & conservation  World weather, climate & climatic change  The Earth & its changing su future  World transport, travel & communications  Farms & the world's food supply  World industry & making goods  The world's resources & their exploitation  The u of the world, population & migration  Homes of the world & the way people live  The world's shops & where they are  Cities of the world & their future  World transp The world's environment & conservation  World weather, climate & climatic change  The Earth & its changing surface  World Geography  People of the world, popu Farms & the world's food supply  World industry & making goods  The world's resources & their exploitation  The world's changing energy supplies  The world's en of the world & the way people live  The world's shops & where they are  Cities of the world & their future  World transport, travel & communications  Farms & the wor weather, climate & climatic change  The Earth & its changing surface  World Geography  People of the world, population & migration  Homes of the world & the wa & making goods  The world's resources & their exploitation  The world's changing energy supplies  The world's environment & conservation  World weather, climate & where they are  Cities of the world & their future  World transport, travel & communications  Farms & the world's food supply  World industry & making goods & its changing surface  World Geography  People of the world, population & migration  Homes of the world & the way people live  The world's shops & where they a exploitation  The world's changing energy supplies  The world's environment & conservation  World weather, climate & climatic change  The Earth & its changing su future  World transport, travel & communications  Farms & the world's food supply  World industry & making goods  The world's resources & their exploitation  The of the world, population & migration  Homes of the world & the way people live  The world's shops & where they are  Cities of the world & their future  World transp The world's environment & conservation  World weather, climate & climatic change  The Earth & its changing surface  World Geography  People of the world, pop Farms & the world's food supply  World industry & making goods  The world's resources & their exploitation  The world's changing energy supplies  The world's en of the world & the way people live  The world's shops & where they are  Cities of the world & their future  World transport, travel & communications  Farms & the wor weather, climate & climatic change  The Earth & its changing surface  World Geography  People of the world, population & migration  Homes of the world & the wa & making goods  The world's resources & their exploitation  The world's changing energy supplies  The world's environment & conservation  World weather, climate & where they are  Cities of the world & their future  World transport, travel & communications  Farms & the world's food supply  World industry & making goods & its changing surface  World Geography  People of the world, population & migration  Homes of the world & the way people live  The world's shops & where they a exploitation  The world's changing energy supplies  The world's environment & conservation  World weather, climate & climatic change  The Earth & its changing su future  World transport, travel & communications  Farms & the world's food supply  World industry & making goods  The world's resources & their exploitation  The of the world, population & migration  Homes of the world & the way people live  The world's shops & where they are  Cities of the world & their future  World transp The world's environment & conservation  World weather, climate & climatic change  The Earth & its changing surface  World Geography  People of the world, pop Farms & the world's food supply  World industry & making goods  The world's resources & their exploitation  The world's changing energy supplies  The world's en of the world & the way people live  The world's shops & where they are  Cities of the world & their future  World transport, travel & communications  Farms & the wor weather, climate & climatic change  The Earth & its changing surface  World Geography  People of the world, population & migration  Homes of the world & the wa & making goods  The world's resources & their exploitation  The world's changing energy supplies  The world's environment & conservation  World weather, climate & where they are  Cities of the world & their future  World transport, travel & communications  Farms & the world's food supply  World industry & making goods & its changing surface  World Geography  People of the world, population & migration  Homes of the world & the way people live  The world's shops & where they a exploitation  The world's changing energy supplies  The world's environment & conservation  World weather, climate & climatic change  The Earth & its changing future  World transport, travel & communications  Farms & the world's food supply  World industry & making goods  The world's resources & their exploitation